SECOND
PROBLEMS

Decimal and metric edition

by

K. A. HESSE

LONGMAN

CONTENTS

LONGMAN GROUP UK LIMITED
Longman House, Burnt Mill,
Harlow, Essex CM20 2JE, England
and Associated Companies throughout the world

© K. A. Hesse 1964

Decimal and metric edition © Longman Group Ltd 1971

First published 1964
Decimal and metric edition first published 1971
Sixteenth impression 1989

Pupil's   ISBN 0 582 18076 7
Teacher's ISBN 0 582 18077 5

Produced by Longman Group (FE) Ltd
Printed in Hong Kong

Answer the following questions with **yes** or **no**:

1. If you add 2 cups to 2 saucers is the answer 4 cups?

2. If you take 3 riders from 4 horses is there one horse left?

3. Is one kilogramme of wood as heavy as one kilogramme of coal?

4. Does $\frac{1}{2}$ litre $+\frac{1}{2}$ litre equal one whole litre?

5. Does $\frac{1}{2}$ apple $+\frac{1}{2}$ orange make one whole fruit?

6. Could a farmer take one half of his flock of 25 sheep from one field and put it into another?

7. Could you place your coat on the middle peg of a row of pegs, $1\frac{1}{2}$ m from the ground, if they were numbered 1 to 12?

8. Is four times eight greater than three times nine?

Tom has more money than John, who has more than Dick.
Complete these sentences by putting in the missing words:

9. Dick has less money than either...   ...or...   ...

10. ...   ... has less than Tom but more than ...   ...

11. ...   ... has more money than either...   ...or...   ...

Write the first fifteen letters of the alphabet across a page of your exercise book.

Under the letters write the numbers 1 to 15 so that 1 is under A, 2 under B, 3 under C and so on.

12. Which letter is sixth?   tenth?   twelfth?

13. What numbers would these groups of letters stand for?

    AB   DE   HH   ABF   HEA   GCB   EIAF

14. Write each answer to these sums as a letter:

    B+C=   F+A+B=   J−H=   G−D=

1. What is the time by this clock?

2. Draw a clock face showing 5 minutes to 9 o'clock. If that is the time for Ann to be at school, how long has she left?

3. Suppose that this clock is 5 minutes fast. Draw a clock face to show what the correct time should be, and write the time in figures—remember it is morning.

4. Suppose that this clock is 5 minutes slow. Draw a clock face to show what the time should be, and write it in figures.

5. Write in figures what the correct time would be if the clock is ten minutes slow.

6. Write in figures what the correct time would be if the clock was twenty minutes fast.

7. Draw a clock face to show what the time was ten minutes before mother waved to Ann, and write the time down in two different ways.

8. Draw a clock face to show what would be the time a half-hour after mother waved. Remember that the hour hand moves as well as the minute hand and give the time in figures.

9. Draw a clock face to show the time three hours later than the time when mother waved.

10. Draw a clock face to show the time three and a half hours later than when mother waved. Remembering that it is after twelve o'clock, write the time in figures.

11. What time is $1\frac{1}{4}$ hours later than 11.30 a.m.?

Look carefully at these groups of dots and numbers:

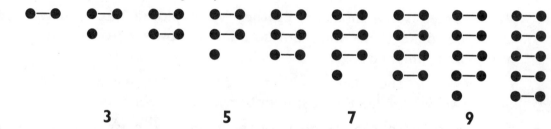

| | 3 | 5 | 7 | 9 |

In 2, 4, 6, 8 and 10 the dots are joined into pairs, having none left over.

Numbers that end in 2, 4, 6, 8, and 0 are called **even numbers**, such as 16, 24, 40, 52 and 78.

In numbers 1, 3, 5, 7 and 9 not all the dots can be paired. Each time we have one left over. We call it the odd one. Numbers that end in 1, 3, 5, 7, and 9 are called **odd numbers**, such as 13, 21, 59, 67 and 95.

1. Pick out the **odd** numbers from these: 10, 12, 9, 15, 36, 31, 17.
2. Write the **even** numbers between 15 and 25.
3. Write the **odd** numbers between 48 and 60.
4. Write the **odd** numbers between 100 and 110.
5. Write the **even** numbers between 205 and 213.

Here are some houses in a part of a street:

6. What should be the number of the house before No. 9?
7. What should be the number of the house after No. 25?
8. Write down the numbers of all the houses before No. 9.
9. How many houses should be built between No. 15 and No. 23?
10. What should be the number of the house opposite No. 1?

Answer each of these sums with **add** or **subtract**.

1. We counted some monkeys as they were placed into a new cage. Later we found there were not so many. How did we find out how many were missing?

2. A boy knew that he had more marbles than when he began a game. How did he find the number he had won?

3. Teacher counted the number of boys in the class and wrote it down. Then he counted the number of girls and wrote that down. How did he find how many pupils were there altogether?

4. Teacher found that there were not so many boys and girls in the class room as there were names on the register. How did he find the number of boys and girls who were absent?

5. When pupils were going to the baths the teacher counted those who went upstairs in the bus and then how many were downstairs. How did he find how many pupils were in the bus?

Work out the answers to these sums in your book.

6. Mother paid 47p for some bacon and 33p for some eggs. What did she pay altogether to the shopkeeper?

7. Mother handed the shopkeeper a pound to pay for the eggs and bacon. How much change did she receive?

8. Father had worked out that their journey to the seaside was going to be 123 kilometres. After travelling for 108 km how much farther had they to go?

9. How high is the top of a window if the frame is 150 cm high and it is fixed 1 metre above the floor?

10. Betty had saved £1·28 towards buying a tie for Father's birthday. The tie she wanted to buy was £2·43. How much more did Betty need?

11. A bus company decides to increase its fleet of 'buses to 150. How many must they add to their present fleet of 128 'buses?

12. John had two dozen marbles and his friend Tom had three score. How many had they altogether?

1. Count how many books there are on the first shelf, then on the second and finally how many are on the third. Set down the numbers and find the total number of books on the shelves. Prove your answer by counting all the books together.

2. How many books must I add to the top shelf to make 20 books altogether?

3. How many must I take from the bottom shelf to leave 8?

4. On the library shelves there were 253 history books, 278 geography books and 204 nature books. What was the total?

Here is a page in a book having 96 pages.

5. How many pages are there in the book after this page?

6. How many pages are there before this page in the book?

7. What can you say about where the book has been opened?

49

ine more than
has been well
ɔns will take
ɪd the ground

---

8. Mother paid 32p for one book, 64p for another and received 4p change. Which coin did mother hand to the bookseller?

9. Had mother paid with a five pound note what change would she have received?

10. Two shelves are to be fixed in the library, one 85 cm long and the other 1 metre long. What length of board is needed?

11. In a novel of 316 pages Tom had read 178 pages. How many more had he to read?

Here are some presents that might be suitable for you to buy for a younger brother or sister on their next birthday.

Here are the values of coins that might be in your money box:

1p   2p   5p   10p   20p   50p   £1

1. Copy the value and then write the name of each coin.

2. You could use only one coin to pay for the skipping rope and receive some change. Name the coin and say how much is the change.

3. Which two coins could you use to pay for a skipping rope?

4. Which two coins can be used to pay for a humming top and say how much change there should be.

5. How much would the trumpet and top together cost?

6. Give the values of the smallest number of coins I could use to pay for them.

7. Is there a toy here which could be paid for by using only one coin without change?

1. Which of these numbers cannot be divided by 3 exactly?
   6   11   15   21   26   31   39   44   48   51

2. Which of these numbers are **odd**?
   48   1   5   21   24   30   37   51

3. Which of these numbers can be divided by 4 exactly?
   6   12   18   20   34   44   54   60   102

Find by how much each of these numbers is separated from the one before it, then say what should be the next number.

4.   2   4   6   8   3   5   7   9

5.   0   3   6   9   1   5   9   13

6.   12   10   8   6   29   25   21   17

7.   5 $4\frac{1}{2}$ 4 $3\frac{1}{2}$ 0 $1\frac{1}{2}$ 3 $4\frac{1}{2}$

8. Write down the even numbers between 40 and 50

If we write C for 2, F for 3, K for 4 and M for 5 find the answer to each of these sums:

9.   C+K   M−F   twice F $\frac{1}{2}$K   C+K−M

10. F×M   K−C   half M $1\frac{1}{2}$C   M−F−C

Write down the number which belongs to each of these words. You may need a dictionary.

11. tricycle   trio   duet   quartet   score

12. decade   decimal   gross   cents   century

With the figures 1 and 2 we can make the numbers 12 and 21.
With the figures 3, 5 and 7 we can make the numbers 357, 375, 573, 537, 753 and 735.

13. Write down all the three-figure numbers you can make by using only 2, 8 and 9.

14. Which was the smallest three-figure number you made with 2, 8 and 9?

15. Write down the smallest three-figure number you can make by using only 0, 4 and 6.

16. Write down the largest three-figure number you can make by using only 0, 1 and 9.

Here is an unfinished sheet from a calendar. Copy this sheet into your exercise book and complete it.

Answer all these questions from the sheet you have made.

1988		JANUARY				1988
S	M	T	W	T	F	S
3	4	5	6	7	8	9

1. On which day of the week is the first of the month?

2. On which day of the week is the last day of the month?

3. What is the date of the last Saturday in the month?
4. Are there more Saturdays than Fridays in the month?
5. On which day falls the 16th?   the 20th?
6. We returned to school after the Christmas Holiday on the second Tuesday of the month. Give its date.
7. How many days were spent in school in this month?
8. If a week's holiday began on 14th January, on which day and date should it end?
9. How many Thursdays are there in this month?
10. What will be the date of the day after the last Sunday in this month?
11. What is the date of the day before the first Friday in January 1988?
12. How many days are there from 25th January to the end of the month?
13. On which day of the week will fall 8th February 1988?
14. On which day of the week will fall 27th December 1987?
15. January is the first month of the year. Say which month is the
      3rd   4th   7th   10th   11th
16. January has 31 days. Which other months of the year have 31 days?
17. If the last two figures of the year divide exactly by 4 it is a Leap Year. Which will be the next Leap Year after 1988?

Measure each of these lines to the nearest millimetre

1. ————————————————————————
2. ————————————————————————
3. ——————————————————————————
4. ——————————————   ——————————
5. ——————————————   ——————

6. Copy this flag into your exercise book: be sure to make all your measurements the same as this.

7. Draw a square with sides of 7 cm 2 mm.

8. Mark the centre of each side and draw lines to join the pairs of opposite marks.

9. How many squares are there altogether in your drawing?

10. Draw a rectangle 9 centimetres by 12 centimetres.
11. Letter it A, B, C and D. Join B to D.
12. On your line BD write "DIAGONAL".
13. How long is the diagonal BD?
14. There is another diagonal.   Give the letters and its length.

Try to make the following measurements:
15. The height of the seat of a pupil's chair.
16. The height of the seat of a teacher's chair.
17. Find how much higher is a teacher's table than a pupil's table.
18. Take one step, or pace, and put a small mark against the heel of each shoe.   Measure your pace.
19. How much less than one metre is your pace?

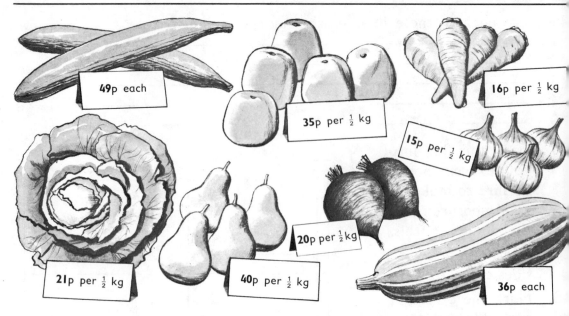

49p each

35p per ½ kg

16p per ½ kg

15p per ½ kg

21p per ½ kg

20p per ½ kg

40p per ½ kg

36p each

Say what change you should receive when handing a fifty pence coin to the shopkeeper for

   1.   a marrow   a cucumber   ½ kg of pears 10p
       1 kg of onions 20p

State the values of three coins which would pay exactly for
   2.   ½ kg of apples 20p, 10p, 5p   1 kg of carrots 20p, 10p, 2p
   3.   1 kg of cabbage   20p, 20p, 2p   2 marrows   50p, 20p, 2p

State the total value of each group:

   4.   ½ kg of apples + ½ kg of beetroot   1 kg of apples
   5.   ½ kg of carrots + 1 marrow   1 kg of onions
   6.   ½ kg of pears + ½ kg of cabbage   ¼kg of beetroot
   7.   1 kg of apples + 1 kg of onions   ¼ kg of carrots
   8.   1 cucumber + 1 cabbage   ½ a marrow
   9.   1 kg of carrots + 1 marrow   1½ kg of beetroot

State what you could buy if the following amounts were the exact payment for goods received:

10.   a fifty

11.   a fifty and a twenty

12.   three twenties

1. How many fifties should you receive in exchange for two pound coins?

2. If I bought three books at 50 pence each, what would be the total cost?

3. If I had four fifties and a one pound coin, how much should I have altogether?

4. State the values of the smallest number of coins with which I can pay an amount of 61p.

5. State the two coins which will give change from a fifty when paying 35p.

6. As a boy was handing £1·65 to a shopkeeper he dropped a coin. If he still had a pound coin, a fifty and a five what was the missing coin?

7. How many 50 pence coins should I add to three pound coins when giving change for a five-pound note?

8. At the bank, silver coins of the same value are packed into paper bags which hold five pounds' worth. How many tens should there be in one of those packed bags?

9. What would be the smallest number of notes and coins worth £7? Write down their values.

10. Write down the values of two coins and two notes which together are worth exactly £11.

11. How many penny coins should you receive in exchange for a twenty?

12. How many twos should you receive in exchange for a fifty?

Here is a number on a gate to a house in a street having houses on both sides.

What should be the numbers on the gates on either side?

Use your dictionary if necessary to find the meanings of these words. Use each one in a sum or sentence so that the meaning is quite plain.

1. double   pair   couple   treble   total

2. smaller   greater   cheaper   dearest   reduce

3. difference   minimum   maximum   product   deduct

We talk of the **depth** of the ocean, the **height** of a mountain, the **length** and **breadth** of a country and the **width** of the highway.

We use these same words in a slightly different way when measuring certain pieces of furniture.

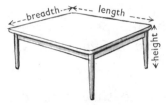

4. Find a table and measure its length, breadth and height.

5. Find a cupboard or set of bookshelves and measure the height, width and depth.

6. Measure the seat of your chair and give the width, depth and height.

Use your dictionary to help in answering these questions:

7. If you require something, are you in need, singing, or making a purchase?

8. Is dimension a shape, a disagreement, something whispered, or a measurement?

9. If you calculate, do you hurry, choose, leave out something, or reckon numbers?

10. If you work out a problem, will it be solved or dissolved?

How is Emperor Augustus connected with 8, the god Janus with 1, the god Mars with 3 and Julius Caesar with 7?

The word **minus** means that a sum includes subtraction. Having **total** in a sum suggests addition.

On your exercise book arrange these four headings:

ADDITION   SUBTRACTION   MULTIPLICATION   DIVISION

Underneath the most suitable of these headings arrange each of the words from this list:

double	reduce	total	product	divisor
quotient	deduct	increase	halve	difference
decrease	altogether	remain	change	share

Each blank in the sentences which follow can be filled by a word from this list. Any word may be used more than once. Write out the word or words required to complete the sentences.

quarter	half	odd	even	difference
equals	minus	total	double	product
multiply	divide	reduce	decrease	increase

1. The first...   ...number after 12 is 14.
2. Thirteen is the...   ...of six and seven.
3. Fourteen is the answer when you...   ...seven.
4. A...   ...of six is three, and a...   ...of ten is five.
5. The...   ...between eleven and eight is three.
6. Twenty-eight is the...   ...of seven and four.
7. The product of 3 and 8...   ...the product of 6 and 4.
8. The answer is 17 when you...   ...twelve by five.
9. The answer is 7 when you...   ...twelve by five.
10. 2 is a...   ...of 8, and 5 is a...   ...of 20.
11. Three is the remainder when you...   ...11 by 4.
12. When we...   ...10 by 3 the answer is the same as when we ...   ...9 by 2.

In FIRST PROBLEMS we dealt with

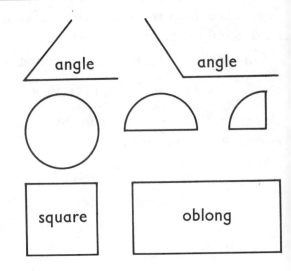

an **angle**, the amount by which two straight lines are turned away from each other at the point where they meet;

a **circle**, which when folded twice gave us an angle, called a **right angle**;

rectangles, which are figures having four straight sides and all the angles right angles. They are square or oblong.

If we draw a diagonal to a square or an oblong, we have new shapes consisting of three straight sides, called **triangles**. Triangles can have angles of many sizes. If one of the angles is a right angle, we call it a **right-angled triangle**.

1. Tear a piece of paper into a circle and fold it twice very carefully to form a right angle.

2. Use your right angle to say which of these triangles is a **right-angled** triangle.

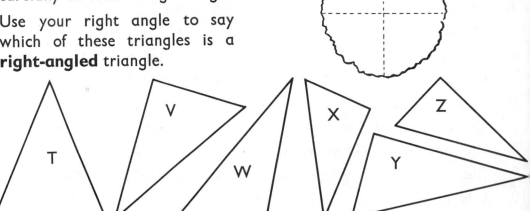

3. Draw two sides to a right angle 4·5 cm and 6 cm long. Join the ends to make a right-angled triangle. How long is the third side?

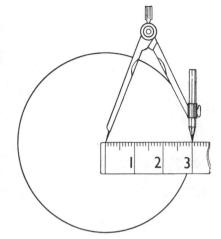

Use a pair of compasses to draw circles of different sizes. Make patterns from overlapping circles and parts of circles.

The steel point forms the **centre** of your circle. The line drawn by the pencil point is called the **circumference**. The distance between the centre and the circumference is the **radius**. The full distance across the centre of the circle to join any two opposite points on the circumference is called the **diameter**. A diameter divides a circle into two halves. Each half is called a **semi-circle**.

Say what must be the radius of a circle when the diameter is

1. 4 cm   10 cm

2. 16 mm   5 m

Say what is the diameter of a circle when the radius is

3. 1 m   9 cm

4. 7 m $5\frac{1}{4}$ m

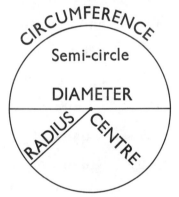

When there is more than one radius we call them **radii.**

5. Draw a circle having a diameter of 8 centimetres.

6. Draw three radii in your circle and measure each one.

7. Draw a circle having a radius of 45 millimetres.

8. Draw three diameters in this circle and measure each one.

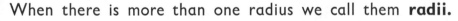

Other shapes enclosed within a curved line are called **ovals**.

In a circle the diameters are equal, but in an oval they are of different lengths.

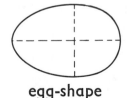

egg-shape

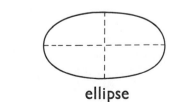

ellipse

1*

1. Write the number which comes immediately before and the one which comes immediately after the following:

9   19   30   90   100   999

Complete:

2.   12= ten and   units   25= tens and   units

3.   41= tens and   units   10= ten and   units

4.   29= tens and   units   30= tens and   units

5.   10= ten or   units   13= ten and   units or   units

6.   50= tens or   units   72= tens and   units or   units

7.   90= tens or   units   99= tens and   units or   units

8.   100=   tens and   units   101=   tens and   units or   units

9.   121=   hundred and   tens and   units or   tens and   units

10. 137=   hundred and   tens and   units or   tens and   units

11. 406=   hundreds and   tens and   units or   tens and   units

12. 328=   units or   tens and   units or   hundreds and   units

13. 249=   units or   tens and   units or   hundreds and   units

14. 500=   units or   tens and   units or   hundreds and   units

How many tens are there in these numbers?

15. 30   17   61   100   385   603   1 000

Write these numbers in order of size, smallest first:

16. 201, 102, 120, 210, 112

Write these numbers in order of size, greatest first:

17. 17, 70, 58, 101, 85

Write the greatest number you can make from each group of figures:

18. 3, 5   1, 3, 2   0, 8, 2   5, 3, 9, 7   0, 6, 4, 9

Write the smallest number you can make from each group of figures:

19. 3, 1, 5   7, 2, 6   0, 7, 6   9, 3, 7, 9
      8, 4, 2, 5

When writing large numbers we leave a small space after millions and after thousands: e.g. 2,506 and 14,786,000. Rewrite these numbers correctly:

1. 2504   41870   167900   8250000

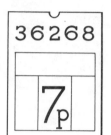

36268

7p

Here is a 'bus ticket. Write down

2. its number in the correct form

3. the real value of the figure "6" between the 2 and the 8.

4. the real value of the figure "6" between the 3 and the 2.

5. the number of the ticket in words.

Look at this part of a poster:

DISTANCES BY PLANE FROM LONDON

Berlin	941 km
Cairo	3,482 km
Moscow	2,499 km
New York	5,520 km
Rome	1,481 km
Darwin	14,363 km

6. Which city is nearest to London?

7. Which city is the farthest from London?

8. Write down in words the value of the figure 4 in the number after
    Berlin   Rome   Darwin

9. How much longer is the journey from London to Cairo than that from London to Moscow?

10. Give the distance of a round trip (there and back) from London to New York.

11. New York is about four times as far from London as Rome is. This is true of two other pairs of cities. Which are they?

Write how many there are:

1. days in 48 hours   weeks in 14 days
2. mins. in $\frac{1}{2}$ hour   days and hours in 36 hours
3. mins. in $1\frac{1}{2}$ hours   seconds in 2 minutes
4. seconds in $\frac{3}{4}$ minute   hours and minutes in 75 min
5. dozens in 24   months before November
6. scores in 40 $1\frac{1}{2}$ dozens in figures
7. 1 gross in figures $1\frac{1}{2}$ scores in figures
8. £1·00 in pence   dozens in a gross
9. tens in a fifty   fifties in £1
10. centimetres in a metre   grammes in a kilogramme
11. millilitres in a litre   203p as pounds
12. centimetre as millimetres   £1·47 as pence
13. number of tens in a hundred   millimetres in a metre
14. metres in $\frac{1}{2}$ kilometre   millilitres in $\frac{1}{2}$ litre

Complete:

15. 107p=£   230p=£   526p=£
16. £3·27=   p   £4·01=   p   £9·10=   p
17. 12 hrs.=   day   36 hr.=   days $\frac{1}{2}$ year=   months
18. $\frac{1}{2}$ gross= $\frac{1}{2}$ gross=   dozens   5 dozen=   score
19. The month immediately after September is
20. The month immediately before March is
21. A home milk bottle holds   times as much milk as a school milk bottle.
22. The radius of a circle is   the length of the diameter.
23. Half a circle is called a
24. The sign that tells us to subtract is called the   sign.
25. The sign that tells us to add is called the   sign.
26. When time is stated in figures we show before noon by adding and after noon by adding

Each answer on this page is to be answered by a word: **yes** or **no**.

1. Is 5 half-way between three and seven?

2. Is $5\frac{1}{2}$ half-way between three and eight?

3. Are there four even numbers between nine and fourteen?

4. Are there three odd numbers between eight and fourteen?

5. Can you use fewer than three coins to equal 13p?

6. Can you have fewer coins to equal 60p than you can have to equal 13p?

7. Is Tuesday the second day of the week?

8. Would a window frame 102 centimetres square fit into an opening in a wall which is one metre square?

9. Could you cut with a saw 3 pieces of wood each exactly 12 cm long from a piece of wood exactly 36 cm long?

10. If letters not over 100 g in weight need a 26p postage stamp, does this mean that a letter weighing 50 g needs a 13p stamp?

11. Is $\frac{1}{5}$ bigger than $\frac{1}{10}$?

12. If you add 0 to 25, does it make it more?

13. If you add a 0 on to a 25, does it make it more?

14. If you add an odd number to another odd number will the answer be an odd number?

15. Is 16 as much below 20 as 26 is above 20?

16. If 1st April is on a Monday should 1st May be on a Tuesday?

17. Is a half-gross more than a half-score?

18. Is three score and ten the same as three times thirty?

19. Are there twelve hours from one o'clock to twelve o'clock?

20. Is one and a half-dozen the same as one and a half dozens?

21. If Mary is six years old and Jane is eleven years old, will Jane be twice as old as Mary next year?

22. John and Jim were born on the same day. John was born at 3 a.m. and Jim was born at 2 p.m. Is Jim older than John?

1. If each of these houses has two people living in it, how many people are there altogether?

2. If there are 3 people in each house, how many people are there altogether?

3. How many people are there altogether in 4 houses if there are 4 people in each house?

4. If two bottles of milk are delivered to each of 5 houses, how many bottles is that altogether?

5. If Mother has three bottles of milk each day in one week, for how many bottles does Mother have to pay each week?

6. If one house has eight doors inside, how many similar doors must a builder order for five similar houses?

Which?

Answer each of the following sums with **add** or **multiply**.

7. Teacher wants each pupil to plant the same number of bulbs in his or her bowl. Say how Teacher will find out how many bulbs have to be ordered.

8. Jill counted the currant buns, Rita counted the plain buns and Janet counted the iced buns. How did Teacher find how many buns there were altogether?

9. It is decided to put the same number of new desks into each classroom. How shall we find how many desks to order?

10. Every week day, except Sunday, a youth delivers the same number of newspapers. How can we find the total number of newspapers delivered by the youth during the six days?

11. As a newsagent counts out the newspapers for each of his news-boys to deliver he writes down the number. How does he find the total number of newspapers that he has counted out?

Write answers only.

1. How much less than thirteen is eleven?

2. Which number is four more than fifteen?

3. What is the sum of seven, two and six?

4. Add three to the sum of eight and two.

5. Tom had thirteen marbles and then won two more. How many did that make altogether?

6. If I take eight books from fourteen books, how many are left?

7. If there are six tennis balls in each of three boxes, how many tennis balls are there altogether?

8. Mary saved 10p each week. After how many weeks can she change her savings for a 50p coin?

9. Father had four bowls into each of which he is going to plant five daffodil bulbs. How many bulbs must he buy?

10. Mary left home at 8.35 a.m. and returned four hours later. At what time was that?

11. If mother cooks 3 eggs for breakfast each morning, how many breakfasts will she cook to use one dozen eggs?

12. How many eggs at 12p each can I buy with 2 twenties and 2 fives?

13. Write down the two even numbers nearest to 10.

14. Which two odd numbers immediately follow nineteen?

15. Remembering how houses in a street are numbered, how many houses are there between No. 5 and No. 11?

16. Suppose that houses in a street are alike on both sides and the first on both sides are opposite each other, what is the number of the house opposite No. 8?

17. If 32 pupils are to be arranged into 4 teams, how many pupils will there be in each team?

18. If a lorry takes 4 metric tonnes of coal on each journey, how many tonnes have been carried altogether on 8 journeys?

Write answers only:

1. 7+ 6=	9−3=	13+5=	4×6=	9×3=
2. 12− 5=	15+8=	12÷4=	27÷9=	28÷7=
3. 23+ 9=	22−7=	6×7=	8×5=	32÷8=
4. 31−27=	45+6=	36÷4=	48÷8=	7×8=
5. 54÷ 9=	8×9=	63÷7=	72÷9=	9×9=

Add:

	cm	£	metres	km	litres
6. 426	3·5	2·08	36·4	2·734	3·62
37	42·6	15·75	8·76	60·8	0·705
509	20·7	0·69	20·94	9·67	0·08
83					

Subtract:

			£	kg	kl
7. 603	5004	2·36	3·82	4·321	1·045
− 74	− 908	−1·43	−1·76	−2·953	−0·948

Multiply:

8.   286   478   2·61   £3·60   5 kg 250 g ×8

        × 7   × 9   × 8   × 6   =   kg

                                                                        × 8

Divide:

                                                                1 km 80 m ÷ 9

9.

6)348   11)100·1   7)1·12   8)£22   = 9)   km

10. Copy this clock and put in the missing minute hand.

Copy this clock and put in the missing hour hand between 8 and 9 o'clock.

11. Write in figures: twenty minutes to ten o'clock at night

Which will always be the greater in number for any person?
1. socks or pairs   gloves or fingers
2. suits or pockets   bicycles or wheels
3. houses or rooms   books or pages

Tom is 8 years old, John is 6 years and Dick is 11 years. Complete:
4. ...   ...is the eldest and...   ...is the youngest.
5. Tom is younger than...   ...but older than ...   ...
6. Both...   ...and...   ...are older than John.
7. Both...   ...and...   ...are younger than Dick.

Think of a visit to buy something at a shop. Complete:
8. The money you had at first
        =the money you spent+the money you...
9. The money you had at first minus the money left
        =the money you...
10. The money you spent plus the money you have left
        =the money you...
11. The money you had at first minus the money you spent
        =the money you...

Study this diagram and then complete the sentence.

□ ─ ─ ─ ─ ─ ─ ─ ─ ─ ─ ─ ─ ─ △ ─ ─ ─ ─ ─ ─ ─ ─ ○
    starting place   resting place   journey's end

12. The distance from the starting place to the resting place, plus the
     distance from the resting place to the journey's end, is equal to
     the total...   ...of the journey.

13. Study this diagram and complete the sums:

□ ─ ─ b ─ ─ ─ △ ─ ─ ─ c ─ ─ ─ ○
$\underbrace{}_{a}$

$a = b +$
$a - b =$
$a - c =$

1. Two 'buses were booked for the journey, one to seat 41 persons and the other to seat 38. How many is that altogether?

2. Three days before the given date there were on the list the names of 6 teachers, 23 pupils from Class 1, 27 from Class 2 and 18 from Class 3. How many was that altogether?

3. How many more names were needed to fill the two 'buses?

4. The charges for hiring the 'buses were £32·50 and £31·75. What was that altogether?

5. The first stop was made after 59 kilometres. If another 24 km completed the journey, how far was it?

6.  These are two sign-posts passed by on the journey. How far is it between them?

7. The journey was due to commence at 9.30 a.m. and the party was expected back by 7 p.m. How long is that?

8. What happened was that the journey commenced at 9.25 a.m. and finished at 7.15 p.m. How long was that?

9. Here is another of the sign-posts which they passed. How far is it between the two cities?

10. One of the places visited was an old abbey. It was built in 1578. How old is it?

11. The abbey has belonged to the present owner and his family since 1788. How long is that?

12. If the abbey stands in grounds which have 438 hectares of parkland and 186 hectares of woods, how big is the estate?

13. The ruins of a cathedral were viewed. It was begun in 1295 and laid in ruins in 1941. How long was that?

If $1+3$ $=2\times2$
and $1+3+5$ $=3\times3$
and $1+3+5+7=4\times4$
what should be equal to $1+3+5+7+9+11$?

When crops in the school garden were ready to be gathered for sale pupils took charge in turn, two at a time.

Tommy Jones and Jim Brown gathered some broccoli and spring cabbage.

1. What was the total value of 6 broccoli at 34p each and 4 kg of spring cabbage at 26p per $\frac{1}{2}$ kg?

2. Jim noticed that there were four rows of broccoli left with 26 in each row. How many was that altogether?

3. Tommy counted the spring cabbage and found that there were 8 where he had been cutting and 37 on the other plot. How many was that altogether?

4. Tommy dug up and cleaned a bunch of leeks weighing $1\frac{1}{2}$ kg. Jim's bunch weighed $\frac{3}{4}$ kg. What was the total weight?

Some new shrubs were delivered at the school and the class were told to check the charges shown on the bill. You check them.

5. Find the cost of 2 Berberis at £2·75 each.

6. Find the cost of 5 Aucuba at £3·25 each.

7. Find the cost of two flowering cherries, one at £4·50 and the other at £5·75.

8. What was the charge for 3 rhododendrons at 85p each?

9. One bundle contained a daphne at £3·25 and a magnolia at What was the total cost of the bundle?

10. Find the cost of a bundle containing 8 azaleas at £3·75 each.

11. What should be the cost of a bundle of three syringas costing £2·50, £2·80, £2·99

12. How much of the border would be taken up by the rhododendrons if each was to be given $1\frac{1}{2}$ metres of space?

1. Bill and Ada bought Mother some flowers. What did they have to pay for nine roses at 38p each?

2. They bought Father an Easter egg. If Bill paid £1·25 towards it and Ada paid £1·65, what did the egg cost?

3. Father's egg was a hollow chocolate one containing chocolates. The shopkeeper said that to buy the egg alone would cost £1·25 and the chocolates alone would cost £1·78. Was it cheaper, dearer or the same to buy the egg with chocolates in it?

4. Father's egg alone contained 210 grammes of chocolate and in it were $\frac{1}{4}$ kg of chocolates. What was the total weight?

5. What would be the total weight of four eggs similar to Father's egg containing the same quantity of chocolates?

6. What would be the total cost of those same four eggs?

When the lady in the shop weighed one of the eggs to show Bill and Ada the weight of the empty egg, she had weights of 2 each of 200 g and 20 g and one each of 100 g, 50 g and 10 g.

7. Which weights did she use for the empty egg? (Look back at the information given in question No. 4.)

8. Which did she use for the full egg?

9. If she had mislaid the 10 g weight, how could she still show that the empty egg weighed 210 g?

10. For breakfast on Easter Sunday Mother boiled one egg each for herself, Bill and Ada and two for Father. If she had paid 12p each for them, what was their total cost?

The space for seating in a theatre widens gradually backwards from the stage, so that each row of seats has one seat at each end extra to the row in front. How many seats should there be in the row fourth from the stage if the front row has 40 seats?

	a	b
Which of these two sums, **a** or **b**, would you work out to answer these problems?	1 8 — 6	6)1 8

1. If a boy walked 18 km in 6 hours, how far did he walk in one hour?

2. A man set out to walk the 18 km from Oldtown to Newtown. He came to a sign-post which said that he was 6 km from Newtown. How far had he walked?

3. Bottles of mineral waters are packed 6 to a carton. How many cartons will be needed to hold 18 bottles?

4. A teapot holds 6 cups of tea. How many times must it be filled in order to pour out 18 cups of tea?

5. The label on a box showed that it had held 18 bars of chocolate. If there were 6 in it, how many had been sold?

6. Rita is 6 years younger than Ann, who is 18 years old. How old is Rita?

7. It was said that Mary, who was 18, was twice as old as Ada who was 6 years old. That was wrong. What should it have been?

8. John arranged his 18 marbles into groups of a half-dozen. How many groups did he have?

From the Library, Betty borrowed a book with 120 pages of text.

9. When she had read 45 pages how many more had she still to read?

10. If she had decided to read 8 pages each day, how many days would it have taken her to read the whole book?

11. Betty decided to read the whole book in five days and the same number of pages each day. How many pages should she read the first day?

The Head Teacher had a box containing one gross of pencils.

12. It was decided to give them out in equal numbers to each of 4 classes. How many did he give to each class?

13. When 72 pencils had been given out how many pencils were still in the box?

The Library records showed that there should be 608 fiction books. On the shelves were 460 and cards showed 139 to be on loan.

1. Do the numbers on the shelves and on loan equal the number that should be in the Library?

2. How many have been lost or mislaid?

Records showed that there should be 1,083 books in the reference section. On the shelves were 857 and 235 were on loan.

3. Have any of the reference books been lost or mislaid?

4. Look back to question 1 and say what the answer to the last question seems to indicate.

5. How many more reference books than fiction books are there in the School Library?

Six extra shelves of equal length are needed in a small recess. A board 630 cm long is used for this purpose.

6. What is the length of each shelf?

Grouping

7. Divide 141 by 6.

8. If 141 tennis balls were to be packed into boxes, each holding 6 balls how many full boxes would there be?

9. How many tennis balls would there be left over?

10. If *all* of the tennis balls were to be sent by a shop-keeper in boxes which held 6 each, how many boxes would he use?

11. If there are 238 pupils staying to school dinner and each table holds 7 pupils, how many tables are needed?

12. How many football teams of eleven players can be picked from 106 boys?

13. How many matches could take place at the same time amongst those teams?

14. If all the boys not playing in these matches were divided into two teams, how many boys would be in each team?

1. If Lily had a ten and a five and spent eight pence, how much would she have left?

2. Mary's rope is 3 metres long. Jane's is half as long again. How long is Jane's rope?

3. Which is greater and by how much, a dozen or a score?

4. If eight buttons have been used from a card which held two dozen, how many buttons should still be on the card?

5. To plant two score cabbages in four equal rows, how many must be placed in each row?

6. State the total weight of 4 books if each weighs 500 grammes.

7. How many fives total fifty pence?

8. What is the difference between 7×8 and 6×9?

9. If May 4th is on Friday, on which day is May 11th?

10. Write in figures: the twenty-third day of October in the year of our Lord nineteen hundred and seventy-two.

11. What change should I receive from a pound after paying for two 'bus fares at 44p each?

12. What is the total value of two ones, three twos and a ten?

13. What must be cut from a metre to reduce it to 85 cm?

14. How long must be a piece of wire to be cut into one dozen pieces each $1\frac{1}{2}$ metres long?

15. What is the total weight of two parcels if one weighs $\frac{1}{2}$ kg and the other weighs $\frac{3}{4}$ kg?

16. Mary had 30p. If her father gave her double that amount, how much would she have?

17. How many customers can each receive a half litre of milk from 4 litres

18. How long was it from 55 B.C. until A.D. 410?

19. If a shopkeeper gave me 17p change in three coins, what would be the values of the coins?

In some shops the goods are ready packed. The packets usually contain weight in kilogrammes or parts of a kilogramme, such as ½ kg (500 grammes), 200 grammes, etc. In other shops goods are weighed when bought.

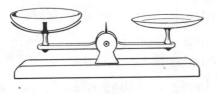

With these scales there could be the following weights.
1 kg,   500 g,   200 g (two), 100 g,   50 g,   20 g (two), 10 g,   5 g.

1. Give the total weight of goods when these weights are used.
    200 g + 50 g   100 g + 50 g + 10 g + 5 g
    500 g + 50 g + 20 g + 5 g   1 kg + 500 g + two 200 g

2. Write what weights would you use to weigh
    70 g   120 g   570 g
    400 g   1½ kg   240 g

3. If a paper bag full of potatoes was put on the scales together with a 10 g weight and they together balanced a 200 g weight, how heavy were the potatoes?

4. Which three weights could I use to weigh ½ kg?

5. A butcher cuts a joint of meat weighing 935 grammes. How much more is needed to make a full kilogramme?

6. What must be taken from a kilogramme to leave 750 g?

7. From a 50 kilogramme sack of potatoes 27 kg and 12·5 kg are sold What weight of potatoes are left?

8. If a metric tonne is the same as a thousand kilogrammes how many 50 kg bags of coal can be filled from a metric tonne of coal?

9. We weigh ourselves in kilogrammes.
    Jennifer is 3 years old, Angela 6 years, Paul 9 years and Mark 12 years. Which of them do you think would have the following weights?:   25·4 kilos   34·7 kilos

10. How much had John gained in weight if he was 37·6 kg at Christmas and 40·3 kg the following August?

Mother paid £9·14 for a roast of beef weighing 2 kilogrammes.

1. How much per kg was charged for the beef?
2. What would be charged for ½ kg of beef at that price?
3. Mother paid for her roast with two five pound notes. What change did she receive?

A bowl of home rendered dripping was labelled at 83p per ½ kg.

4. What would be charged for 500 grammes?
5. What would be charged for a quarter kilogramme?
6. What change from five tens should you receive when paying for 250 grammes?

Sausages were labelled at 73p per half kilogramme.

7. What is that per kilogramme?
8. If a packet of sausages was found to weigh ¼ kilogramme, what should be the price of the packet?
9. What would 1½ kg of sausage cost?

Pork was labelled at £1·18 per half kilogramme.

10. Mother bought 6 pork chops for £3·12. What does that work out for one chop?
11. If the chops were much the same in size, would one of them weigh more or less than 250 grammes?

A leg of lamb is marked at £1·40 per ½ kg and when weighed was shown to be exactly two kilogrammes.

12. A customer asked for the leg to be boned. It then weighed 1¾ kg. What was the weight of the bone?

13. What was the charge for the bone, since it is included in the price for the leg of lamb?

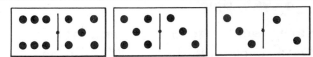

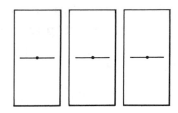

Draw these three dominoes rearranged as shown on the right, but placed so that the total of the dots in the upper portions is equal to the total of the dots in the lower portions.

1. What part of each shape is shaded?

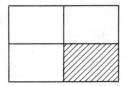

Complete:

2. $\frac{1}{2}$ hour =   minutes $\frac{1}{4}$ hour =   minutes $\frac{3}{4}$ hour =   minutes

3. $\frac{1}{4}$ year =   months $\frac{3}{4}$ year =   months $\frac{3}{4}$ of 20p =   pence

4. $\frac{1}{2}$ 3 kilos =   kilos $1\frac{1}{2}$ min. =   seconds $1\frac{1}{4}$ hours =   minutes

Which of these cannot be made into halves or quarters?

5. cakes   cows   sheep   bars of chocolate   metres

6. pigs   eggs   balloons   buckets of water   boys

Write down what is one-half of

7. 4 sheep   6 cows   12 eggs   8 nuts

8. 3 metres   5 kilos   9 litres   7 hours

Write down what is one-quarter of

9. 8 hens   5 metres   9 hours   12 eggs

10. 10 litres   6 metres   17 kilos   13 litres

11. If your Head Teacher asks your Class Teacher to send a half of the class to be examined by the nurse, how many children will go?

12. If a quarter of the class at a time is to go to the nurse, write down how many should go each time.

13. When Tom, Dick and Harry went into a café for lunch Tom said he would pay one-half and Dick said he would pay one-half. If the total for the meal came to £4·90, say how much each of them paid

14. What will be the number if 106 is made a half as big again?

1. If you break this bar of chocolate into halves, how many sections will there be in each half?

2. If you break it into quarters, how many sections will there be in each quarter?

3. If you eat one-quarter of it, how many sections will be left?

4. What fraction of the bar will be left if you eat $\frac{1}{4}$ of it?

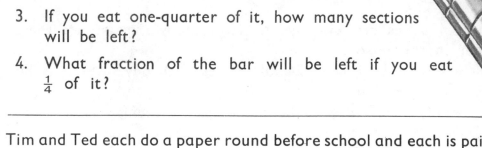

Tim and Ted each do a paper round before school and each is paid £7·20 per week. Tim decides to save one-half of his and Ted decides to save one-quarter of his.

5. How much does each boy save per week?

6. How much will each have saved after four weeks?

In the needlework class was a card on which were 12 buttons.

7. If the teacher told Ann to use one-half of them, how many would be left?

8. If the teacher said that Ann would need all on the card and half as many again, how many buttons would Ann use?

A baker was asked to bake 512 cakes for the school parties and to deliver half of them on Tuesday and the rest on Wednesday.

9. How many cakes would the baker deliver on Wednesday?

When they arrive at the Fair Ann has £2·28 and Jane has £2·36. They decide to put all their money together and share it.

10. What is the total amount of their money?

11. How much will each have when it is shared?

12. Each decides to save one-quarter of her share to pay for the 'bus fare home and for some crisps. What does each save?

Which of these four sums, **a**, **b**, **c** or **d**, would you work out to find the answers to these problems?

a	b	c	d
24	24	24	
+ 4	× 4	− 4	4)2 4

1. In each of 4 boxes are 24 crayons. How many crayons are there altogether in the boxes?
2. A cyclist keeps fit by cycling 24 kilometres each day. What is his total distance after 4 days?
3. 24 children in a class are to be made into 4 teams. How many should there be in each team?
4. If 24 rose trees are to be planted in 4 rows, how many trees should there be in each row?
5. 24 tulip bulbs are planted, but 4 fail to flower. How many flowers are there to be cut?
6. A boy won four marbles from his friend. He started the game with 24 marbles. How many marbles does he now have?

7. How many millilitres are there in

   2 litres? $\frac{1}{2}$ litre? $\frac{1}{4}$ litre?

8. How many 200 ml bottles can be filled from 1 litre of milk?
9. A half-litre jug will fill 2 cups and still contain 100 ml. How much does each cup hold?

10. How many centimetres are there in

    $\frac{1}{2}$ metre? $\frac{1}{4}$ metre? $1\frac{1}{2}$ metres?

11. How many metres are there in

    200 cm?   50 cm?   350 cm?

12. How many weeks are there from 2nd March to 30th March?
13. If a boy delivers one hundred and one newspapers each day, how many will he deliver in one full week?

1. How many boxes will be needed to pack 405 tennis balls if each box holds nine balls?

2. At a concert hall 206 tickets were bought in advance and 98 people paid at the door. How many people paid?

3. How many sevens are equal to two hundred and three?

4. Will eight go exactly into three hundred and forty?

5. How many pupils are absent from a school of 460 pupils if there are 408 pupils present?

6. By how much is nine hundred greater than seven hundred and ninety-three?

7. During an air race an aeroplane has to fly six times around a course of 208 kilometres. How far is the race?

8. If each of seven 'buses can take fifty-eight children, how many can go on an outing to the seaside in these 'buses?

9. Into how many groups of nine can three hundred and six tulips be arranged?

10. How many daffodils will be needed to make up 450 bunches, each having one dozen blooms?

11. A man decides that for a wall he will have to lay eleven courses of bricks with one hundred and twenty-eight bricks in each course. How many bricks will be needed?

12. How many sheep must a farmer add to his flock of 208 sheep to bring it up to a flock of 400?

13. A motorist drove for 196 kilometres on Thursday and for 207 on Friday. How far did he travel in those two days?

14. The milkman delivers 308 bottles of milk to the school on five days of the week. What is the week's total?

15. How many full boxes of flowers will there be if 1,500 bunches are packed into boxes having 9 bunches in each box?

A class of 39 pupils arrived at the enclosed yard outside the dairy. Three foremen were to show them round in equal groups at the same time. Each group was to spend about $1\frac{1}{2}$ hours at the dairy.

  1. How many pupils would there be in each group?
  2. What would be the total time given by the group of foremen?
  3. What would be the total time spent at the dairy by the class?

Before leaving the yard the pupils saw a lorry that had just arrived with a complete load of churns, each full and holding 40 litres. On the lorry were 16 rows of churns with 5 in each row.

  4. How many churns were on the lorry?
  5. How much milk would 10 churns hold?
  6. How much milk altogether would all the churns on that lorry hold? Give your answer in litres.

The pupils were told that 12 litres of milk were needed to produce one litre of thick cream.

  7. How many litres of milk would produce $\frac{1}{2}$ litre of cream?
  8. How much cream would three litres of milk produce?
  9. If an hotel ordered $1\frac{1}{2}$ litres of cream, how many litres of milk would be needed to produce it?

It was also stated that the cream from 22 litres of milk was needed to produce one kilogramme of butter.

State how many litres of milk would be needed to produce

  10. three kilogrammes of butter   half a kilogramme
  11. 250 grammes of butter   100 kilogrammes

State how much butter would be produced from

  12. 44 litres of milk   220 litres of milk
  13. 2·2 litres of milk   0·22 litres of milk

If milk at home costs 25p per bottle state the cost of

  14. 2 bottles   7 bottles   100 bottles

Jugs, cups, barrels, buckets, bottles, etc., are all vessels which hold liquids. The amount each will hold is called its capacity. Here is a list of some liquids you know and some of the ways they are measured.

KILOLITRES   Water in a tank or reservoir.

LITRES OR   Oil, petrol, milk, etc.
PARTS OF A LITRE

MILLILITRES   Medicine, milk in bottles, etc.

Remember: 1 kilolitre = 1 000 litres   (2 home bottles of milk hold
          1 litre = 1 000 millilitres   a little more than 1 litre)

1. If a tumbler holds $\frac{1}{4}$ litre, say how many litres of milk will be needed to fill

   4 tumblers   8 tumblers   2 tumblers   6 tumblers

2. A measuring jug holds one litre. It has five divisions marked on it. What amount does each division represent?

3. A teapot holds 800 millilitres when full and is enough for 4 cups. How much should each cup hold?

4. When two cups have been poured, how much should be left in the teapot? Answer in millilitres.

5. How much should be left, in millilitres, after pouring out
        1 cup?   3 cups?   4 cups?

6. A car will travel 8 kilometres on a litre of petrol. How far will it travel on 10 litres?   12 litres?

7. How many litres will it need to travel 40 kilometres?
                                        60 kilometres?

8. One Monday the school water meter showed 18 598 litres. On the following Monday the reading was 30 053 litres. How much water had been used during the week?

Measure these lines and say what half their length would be.

1. ————————————————————————————

2. ————————————————————————

3. —————————————————————————————————

4. ———————————————————————————————

5. What length would be a quarter of the line in Nos. 1 and 3?

Complete:

6. $1\frac{1}{2}$ cm -1 cm $=$ cm $1\frac{1}{2}$ cm $-\frac{1}{2}$ cm $=$ cm $1\frac{1}{2}$ cm $-1\frac{1}{2}$ cm $=$ cm

7. $1\frac{1}{2}$ l $-\frac{1}{4}$ l $=$ l $1\frac{1}{2}$ l $-\frac{3}{4}$ l $=$ l $1\frac{1}{2}$ l $-1\frac{1}{4}$ l $=$ l

8. 6 months $=$ year   3 months $=$ year   9 months $=$ year

9. $1\frac{1}{4}$ hr. $-\frac{1}{2}$ hr. $=$ hr. $1\frac{1}{2}$ kg $-\frac{1}{4}$ kg $=$ kg $1\frac{1}{2}$ hr. $-\frac{3}{4}$ hr. $=$ hr.

10. $1\frac{1}{4}$ hr. $+\frac{1}{2}$ hr. $=$ hr. $\frac{3}{4}$ hr. $+\frac{3}{4}$ hr. $=$ hr. $1\frac{1}{2}$ m $-1\frac{1}{4}$ m $=$ m

11. $1\frac{1}{4}+\frac{3}{4}=$ $\frac{3}{4}+\frac{1}{2}=$ $2\frac{3}{4}+\frac{3}{4}=$

12. What is a half of a half?

13. A churn when full will hold 40 litres. It is now three-quarters full. How many litres are needed to fill it?

14. How many cans full would I need to fill it up if the can holds $2\frac{1}{2}$ litres?

15. A packet of fertilizer holds 500 grammes. A man buys 3 packets. What weight of fertilizer did he buy in kilogrammes?

16. If a boy spent half of his pocket money and lost half of what he had left, what part of his pocket money did he still have?

17. A plumber went to repair a pipe. He was away for $2\frac{1}{2}$ hours. If travelling to and from the job took $\frac{3}{4}$ hour, how long did it take to do the job?

If a store-keeper had 42 left foot boots and 38 right foot boots of the same size, how many pairs of boots can he make up from them?

1. On the outward journey Tom saw that the 'bus was made to carry 56 passengers. If all seats were full and seven people were standing, how many were on the 'bus?

2. On the return journey in the same 56 seater 'bus Tom saw that all seats downstairs were full, but heard the conductor say that there was room for eight passengers upstairs. How many people were on the 'bus?

3. Tom noticed that the 'bus took 4 minutes to reach a place which his Father told him was exactly one kilometre from where he had boarded the 'bus. How far would the 'bus travel for one hour at the same speed?

4. If Tom started on his outward journey at 10 a.m. and arrived at his destination at 20 minutes to 11 o'clock, how long had the journey taken?

5. If the return journey commenced at 3.45 and ended at half-past four o'clock, how long had the journey taken?

6. If the 56 seater 'bus made eight journeys in one day, what is the total number of seated passengers it would carry in one day for full journeys?

7. If each of those eight journeys had been made with all seats occupied and four passengers standing, what would be the total number of passengers carried?

8. The total travelling time on those 8 journeys was 208 minutes. What does that work out for one journey?

9. The conductor told Tom that 7 'buses on the following day were taking 371 children to a zoo. How many would there be to each 'bus?

10. 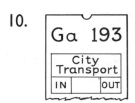 Here is the first ticket and the return ticket issued to Tom. How many of these tickets had the conductor issued after Tom had received his first ticket?

11. The 'bus used 10 litres of diesel oil for travelling 45 kilometres. How many kilometres is that for one litre of diesel oil?

A Visit to a Farm

Tom and Ann went to stay with cousin John on his father's farm. It took them 6 minutes by 'bus from home to the station, they waited 3 minutes for the train, on which they travelled for 40 minutes, and a 5-minute walk took them to the farm.

1. The two children were visiting relatives. What relation was the farmer and his wife to Tom and Ann?

2. What was the total time taken by Tom and Ann to travel from home to the farm?

3. At what time did the 'bus leave if it was 5 minutes late and should have left at 2.58 p.m.?

4. At what time did the train leave?

5. At what time did the train arrive at the country station?

Uncle Joe had 96 ewes, 2 rams and 157 lambs.

6. What was the total number of sheep on the farm?

7. If 9 of the fatter lambs were sold, how many sheep were left?

8. If those lambs were sold for £34 each, how much money did Uncle obtain for them?

9. If Uncle Joe put that amount to buying 9 ewes at £42 each, and 8 at £45 each, what did he spend on them?

10. How big was the flock when the new ewes were added?

One morning Tom and Ann counted the poultry. There were 23 ducks, 78 hens and cockerels, 106 young chickens and 10 geese.

11. What was the total number of poultry?

12. That day the geese were sold for £7·75 each. How much did Uncle Joe receive for them?

13. One morning foxes killed some young chickens. There were 68 left alive in the pen. How many young chickens had the foxes killed?

14. If each of those young chickens was worth £3, what was the total value of Uncle Joe's loss?

There were 73 laying hens. Ann kept a record for the days when she helped Auntie to collect and clean the eggs. On Monday there were 64, on Tuesday 68, on Wednesday 73 and Thursday 59.

15. On which day was the egg production at its lowest?

16. On which day was the egg production at its maximum?

17. What was the total egg production for those four days?

18. How many dozens equal that quantity?

19. If the eggs were sold by the shopkeeper at 12p each, what was that per dozen?

20. If Auntie sold them to the shopkeeper at £1·10 per dozen, how much profit did the shopkeeper make per dozen?

While helping with the cattle Tom noted that the milk yield was 400 litres on Monday, 396 on Tuesday, 390 on Wednesday and 405 on Thursday.

21. On which day was the yield least?

22. On which day was the yield greatest?

23. What was the difference between the maximum yield and the minimum yield for those four days?

24. If the milk is put into forty litre churns, how many churns were needed on Monday?

A man who was laying a hedge was a craftsman paid at the rate of £25 for every ten metres he completed. The hedge was 80 metres long.

25. How much per metre was he being paid?

26. What was the total charge for laying Uncle Joe's hedge?

1. Write in figures (a) Nine thousand, nine hundred and nine.
    (b) Ten thousand, and ten.

2. The numbers in this cross can be moved
    around so that when you add the column of
    three numbers the answer is the same as
    when you add the row of five numbers. There
    are several ways of arranging the numbers.
    Try to find two ways.

    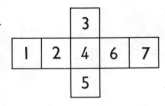

3. Is there any difference between twice twenty-five and twice five and
    twenty?

4. Is there any difference between one and a half-dozen and one and a
    half dozens?

5. How many odd numbers, each of two figures, can you make from
    the figures 1, 2 and 3?

6. There are several ways of arranging four threes so that the
    answer is 0. Here is one: $3+3-3-3=0$. Can you find other
    ways of arranging the plus and minus signs to give the same result?

7. Can you put in the plus and minus signs to complete this sum?
    $$2\ \ 2\ \ 2\ \ 2=4$$

8. Look carefully at these division by nine sums:

    $20\div9=2\ r\ 2$ $30\div9=3\ r\ 3$
    $200\div9=22\ r\ 2$ $800\div9=88\ r\ 8$
    $2,000\div9=222\ r\ 2$ $4,000\div9=444\ r\ 4$

    Without carrying out the division sum write the answers to these:
    $40\div9=$ $700\div9=$ $5,000\div9=$

9.

1	2	3
4	5	6
7	8	9

    Here is a large square divided into nine
    equal squares which are numbered.
    Draw similar squares and put in the
    figures 1 to 9 arranged in such a way
    that when each row is added, when each
    column is added, and then each group

	7	2
	5	
	3	

    taken diagonally is added, the totals are all the same. The squares
    on the right show how to begin.

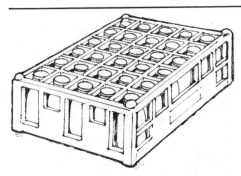

Schools used to have free milk delivered in crates like this.

1. How many bottles are there in each short row?
2. How many short rows of bottles are there?
3. How many bottles of milk are there altogether?
4. If a class requires 27 bottles of milk, how many bottles in the crate will remain untouched?

Each of these bottles holds an ordinary cupful of milk. Each is much smaller than the bottle of milk delivered to your door at home.

5. When anything is divided or shared into two **equal** parts, what do we call each part?
6. When anything is divided or shared into four **equal** parts, what do we call each part?
7. Write in figures: one-half   one-quarter   three-quarters

Three of the bottles of milk delivered to schools were equal to one home bottle.

One home bottle filled **three** school milk bottles. That bottle of milk is divided into **three equal parts.**

When anything is divided or shared into 3 equal parts each part is called one **third** and written in figures $\frac{1}{3}$.

8. Write in figures: two-thirds.
9. How many school bottles of milk equal one home bottle?
10. How many school bottles of milk equal two home bottles?
11. How many school bottles can be filled from 3 home bottles? .
12. How many school bottles can be filled from 2 home bottles?
13. How many thirds are there in 5 of anything?
14. How many thirds are there in 7 of anything?
15. How many home bottles are needed to hold the milk in one full crate?
16. $\frac{1}{3}+\frac{1}{3}=$ $\frac{2}{3}+\frac{1}{3}=$ $\frac{2}{3}+\frac{2}{3}=$ $1-\frac{1}{3}=$ $1-\frac{2}{3}=$

1. Dora had 84p when Uncle gave her 37p. How much did that make?

2. Father bought a cricket bat for £4·25 and a set of stumps for £2·97. How much more did the bat cost than the wickets?

3. How much change from a twenty pound note should Mother have after paying £18·84 for a pair of shoes?

4. If the teacher paid £9·94 for 7 copies of the same book, what is the value of one of these books?

5. What should be the value of eight atlases if one costs £1·37

6. What is the difference in price between a cycle costing £109 and another costing £145

7. £1·18 will buy 200 g of chocolates. What should you have to pay for a half kilogramme of chocolates?

The baker calls on Mother on four days each week and each time she takes two loaves. Each loaf costs 54p

8. How many loaves per week does Mother take?

9. What is the total cost of the bread for one week?

A youth is paid £5 per week for delivering papers plus 3p for each place of delivery. He delivers papers at 76 homes.

10. How much does he receive for delivery payments?

11. What is his total payment for one week?

The milkman leaves one bottle of milk on each day except on Sunday, when he leaves three.

12. How many bottles of milk are delivered in one week?   9 bottles

13. If the charge is 25p per bottle, what is the bill for one week?

A newsboy delivers a morning and an evening newspaper at 25p each on weekdays and on Sundays a newspaper at 40p. He also brings one magazine each week at 32p and another at 38p.

14. Find the cost of the newspaper from Monday to Saturday.

15. What is the total cost of the newspapers and magazines delivered during the whole of one week?

Write these numbers to the nearest ten:
1. 8   27   53   55   95   124   276

How many will be left over when packing in boxes of ten?
2. 27 marbles   86 peaches   123 balls   325 pears

How many more do I need so that none are left over when packing in boxes of ten?
3. 35 marbles   17 peaches   94 balls   266 pears

Write in figures:
4. three tens and six units   seven tens and no units
5. eleven tens and five units   twenty-one tens and no units
6. three hundreds, four tens and nine units
7. seven hundreds, no tens and eight units
8. four hundreds and twenty-three units

To 34 add
9. 3 units   6 units   8 units   2 tens   7 tens

From 156 subtract
10. one hundred   six units   five tens   eight tens

Write the following numbers under the column headings:
H T U   H T U
11. twenty-three   six hundred and four
12. thirty   sixty
13. three hundred   six
14. How many times greater does the three become as it moves one place to the left from the units column to the tens column?
15. How many times greater does the three become as it moves one place to the left from the tens column to the hundreds column?
16. How many times less does the six become as it moves one place to the right from the hundreds column to the tens column?
17. How many times less does the six become as it moves one place to the right from the tens column to the units column?
18. How many times greater does the three become as it moves two places to the left?
19. How many times less does the six become as it moves two places to the right?

Note that 3 moved one place to the left becomes 30 and £0·50 moved one place to the left becomes £5.

1. Write the new numbers formed by these by moving the figures one place to the left:

   5   9   12   35   40   50   816

2. Write the new amounts formed from these by moving the figures one place to the left:

   £1·32   £0·65   £2·70   £0·89   £0·40

Note that 20 moved one place to the right becomes 2 and £5 moved one place to the right becomes £0·50.

3. Write the new numbers formed from these by moving the figures one place to the right:

   50   70   280   300   6 000   190   40

4. Write the new amounts formed from these when the figures are moved one place to the right:

   £12·60   £23   £47   £3·40   £0·80

Complete the following:

5. When the figures in a number are moved one place to the left the value of that number is made   times greater.

6. When the figures in a number are moved two places to the left the value of that number is made   times

7. When the figures in a number are moved one place to the right the value of that number is made   times less.

8. When the figures in a number are moved two places to the right the value of that number is made   times

9. To change metres to centimetres we move the figures   places to the left, so that 2 metres =   centimetres.

10. To change centimetres to metres we move the figures   places to the right, so that 300 centimetres =   metres.

Complete:

1. To make a number ten times greater is the same as to   it by 10.

2. To make a number 100 times greater is the same as to   it by 100.

3. To make a number 10 times less is the same as to   it by 10.

4. To make a number 100 times less is the same as to   it by 100.

5. To move a number one place to the left is the same as to   it by .

6. To move a number one place to the right is the same as to   it by .

7. State what we call each part when we divide an apple into

   2 equal parts   3 equal parts   5 equal parts

   7 equal parts   8 equal parts   10 equal parts

8. If we divide a banana into ten equal parts one part is a

Look carefully at this number: H T U

                                 5 4 1

By moving it one place to the right we divide it by 10 and the answer is

          H T U

          5 4 and 1 unit over.

9. If we divide that 1 unit by ten we get

10. If we divide three units by ten we get

As we use a point to separate parts of a pound from unit pounds so we use a DECIMAL POINT to separate tenths from units instead of writing a vulgar fraction.

                                                    H T U · t

Look at this number: $52\frac{3}{10}$ becomes   5 2 · 3

                    and $106\frac{7}{10}$ becomes   1 0 6 · 7

We say, "Fifty-two point three and one hundred and six point seven."

Write each of these numbers as a decimal fraction:

11. $34 \div 10 =$ $51 \div 10 =$ $248 \div 10 =$ $109 \div 10 =$

Complete, writing your answers as decimals:

1. $23 \div 10 =$ $40 \div 10 =$ $201 \div 10 =$ $308 \div 10 =$
2. $1 \cdot 2 \times 10 =$ $3 \cdot 7 \times 10 =$ $10 \cdot 2 \times 10 =$ $0 \cdot 6 \times 10 =$
3.   When we divide a unit by ten we call the parts
4.   When we divide a unit by one hundred we call the parts

That gives us another column:

Write under column headings: H T U · t h

5.   two units, four tenths and one hundredth.
6.   five units, six tenths and two hundredths.
7.   six units, no tenths and five hundredths.
8.   no units, seven tenths and eight hundredths.
9.   ten units, no tenths and nine hundredths.
10.   twenty-three point five four.
11.   thirty-seven point nine eight.
12.   forty point two six.
13.   eighteen point nought five.
14.   nought point seven eight.

Write these vulgar fractions as decimals. When there is not a units-figure before the decimal point we put in a place-holder 0.

15. $1\frac{3}{10}$ $\frac{3}{10}$ $1\frac{19}{100}$ $2\frac{27}{100}$ $\frac{27}{100}$ $\frac{71}{100}$

When there is no figure for the tenths column we put in a place-holder zero.

Write these vulgar fractions as decimals:

16. $1\frac{17}{100}$ $1\frac{7}{100}$ $\frac{7}{100}$ $2\frac{9}{100}$ $\frac{19}{100}$ $\frac{9}{100}$
17. $5\frac{3}{10}$ $5\frac{3}{100}$ $\frac{3}{10}$ $\frac{3}{100}$ $\frac{9}{10}$ $\frac{8}{100}$

Look at this number: $46 \cdot 85$

State the value of the figures:

18.   6   8   4   5

To $46 \cdot 85$ add:

19.   100   20   8 $\frac{1}{10}$ $\frac{2}{10}$ $\frac{3}{100}$

1. How long is this line?

 _____

2. What would be the total length of ten such lines placed end to end? Write your answer in two ways.

State in another way

3. 1 000 metres   500 metres

4. $\frac{1}{10}$ of 1 metre $\frac{1}{100}$ of 1 metre

5. $\frac{1}{10}$ of 1 kilometre $\frac{7}{10}$ of 1 kilometre

6. $\frac{1}{100}$ of 1 kilometre $\frac{3}{100}$ of 1 kilometre

7. $\frac{1}{10}$ of 1 centimetre $\frac{3}{10}$ of 1 centimetre

8. Draw a line more than eight and a half centimetres long, but less than 9 centimetres, and write its length in two ways.

9. Draw a line more than ten centimetres long but less than ten and a half centimetres, and write its length in two ways.

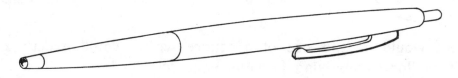

10. Measure the total length of this ball-point pen and write its length (a) to the nearest millimetre, and (b) to the nearest centimetre.

11. Measure to the nearest centimetre the length and the width of (a) this page and (b) a page of your exercise book.

12. State these measurements to the nearest metre:
    6 m 7 cm   12 m 17 cm   30 m 57 cm
    100 m 53 cm

13. State these measurements to the nearest kilometre:
    3 km 49 m   9 km 78 m   10 km 306 m
    20 km 803 m

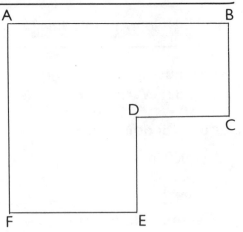

1. Copy this shape into your book,

2. Put a cross in each right angle of your drawing.

3. Draw the diagonal AC.

4. How long is AC?

5. What can you say about the length of BC, CD and DE?

6. If I drew two similar circles to this and cut them out, how far would they reach, placed flat and edge to edge?

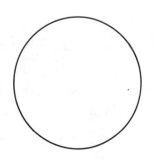

7. How far would 5 similar circles reach if placed in a straight line, edge to edge?

8. Arrange 7 coins so that six, edge to edge, form a ring round the seventh. If circles similar to this were arranged so, what would be the greatest distance across the ring?

9. What would be the size of a square which would exactly contain four similar circles lying flat and edge to edge?

10. What would be the size of an oblong which would exactly contain two of these circles lying flat and edge to edge?

11. Why is it that a square is a rectangle but a rectangle is not necessarily a square?

12. Does one diagonal always divide a rectangle into halves?

13. How many triangles are there formed when one diagonal of a rectangle is drawn?

14. How many triangles are there formed when two diagonals of a rectangle are drawn? (Try out a sketch.)

15. What can you say about a triangle formed by drawing one diagonal of a square?

1. Three brothers measure their height. Sidney put 1·51 m, Vincent put 124½ cm and Arthur put 1·29 m. Which of the brothers is (a) the shortest, (b) the tallest, and (c) by how much is the one taller than the other?

2. How long should a board be in metres to provide enough wood to make five shelves each 70 cm long?

3. Seven ribbons, each 126 cm long, are needed for costumes in a play. How many whole metres of ribbon must be ordered?

4. Allowing 50 cm for each person, what width of space will be needed to seat 11 people?

5. A piece of wood 1·2 m long, when cut in half, will make the two opposite sides of a box. How long will be the box?

6. A length of board 2·76 m long is to be cut into four equal pieces to make shelves. How long will each shelf be?

7. A piece of braid is 5·6 m long. How long will be each piece for drill bands if the braid is cut into 7 equal lengths?

8. How much must be added to 89½ cm to make one metre?

9. How much must be cut off a length of pipe 2·16 m long, to leave it 1·8 m long?

10. How many 10 cm tiles, edge to edge, equal 2 metres?

11. How many 10 cm tiles will reach along a wall 3½ m long?

12. How high will twelve rows of 15 cm tiles reach?

13. The bottom of a box is covered with 15 cm tiles, fitted edge to edge. They are arranged in 4 rows with 5 tiles in each. Give the length and width of the inside of the box.

14. What height and width of a wall is covered with ten rows of tiles having seventy 10 cm tiles in each row?

15. How far will reach 11 paving slabs, each 75 cm long?

16. A shelf is 1·86 m above the floor of a room. Mick is 128 cm tall. There is a stool 56 cm high on which he stands. Does Mick's head reach the shelf?

1. How many millilitres are there in: a litre? $\frac{1}{2}$ litre?

2. How many 100 ml bottles can be filled from a litre?

3. Medicine should be taken in doses of 5 ml twice a day. If the medicine bottle holds 100 ml, how long will the medicine last?

4. Two tumblers were filled from $\frac{1}{2}$ litre and there was enough left to fill a 100 ml bottle. How much did each tumbler hold?

5. A litre can of oil was knocked over. What was left filled 4 small cans, each holding 100 ml. How much oil was spilled?

6. 100 ml of water is needed to make a cake.
    Write how you could use a $\frac{1}{2}$ litre bottle and a 200 ml cream bottle to measure the 100 ml that is needed.

7. How can one measure a litre of water with a 600 ml bottle and a 200 ml bottle?

8. From an oil can holding $1\frac{1}{2}$ litres, 600 ml have been used. How much is left?

9. A petrol tank holds 30 litres when three quarters full. How many litres would it hold when full?

10. When 20 litres of petrol have been taken from a tank it is found to be two thirds full. What does the tank hold when full?

11. One bottle of orange squash makes 15 glasses of orangeade. If a glass equals 200 ml, how many litres of orangeade can be made from one bottle of orange squash?

12. A can, which is $\frac{3}{4}$ full, will hold 80 litres when full. How many litres are needed to fill it?

When blackberrying, Jim and his three sisters each filled the can that they had been given. Jim's can held a litre and Mary's a $\frac{1}{2}$ litre. Betty's can held 350 ml but Jane's only 150 ml.

13. How many litres of blackberries had they collected between them?

14. If 400 ml of blackberries were needed to make a pie, how many pies could be made?

A bunch of 5 bananas weighed $\frac{1}{2}$ kg. We would expect 2 of them to weigh nearly $\frac{1}{4}$ kg. A half kilogramme of bananas would cost 38p

1. About how much would 2 bananas cost?

2. About how much would 10 bananas cost?

3. What would be the approximate cost of a bunch of 7 or 8 bananas?

4. What would be the approximate cost of a bunch of 13 bananas?

A roll of ribbon is marked at 60p per metre.

5. State the cost of $\frac{1}{2}$m $1\frac{1}{2}$m $\frac{1}{4}$m $\frac{3}{4}$m $1\frac{3}{4}$m

Tomatoes are marked at 90p per kilogramme.

6. What would be the cost of $\frac{1}{2}$ kg?   2 kg? $1\frac{1}{2}$ kg?   3 kg?

7. What would be the change from £1·50 when paying for $1\frac{1}{2}$ kg of tomatoes?

Eggs are marked at £1·22 per dozen or 11p each.

8. What would you expect to pay for 6 eggs?

9. What should you pay for three eggs?

10. What do you save by buying your eggs a dozen at one time instead of buying a dozen in oddments?

11. What would be the cost of eighteen eggs?

Pre-cooked chicken is sold at 72p per $\frac{1}{2}$ kg. Chickens weighing about $1\frac{1}{2}$ kg are divided into quarters and sold at 59p per portion.

12. What sould be the charge for $1\frac{1}{2}$ kg chicken?

13. What change would there be from £5 when paying for it?

14. For what would the whole of a divided chicken be sold?

15. What saving is there in buying a whole chicken rather than buying four portions?

16. How much extra does the shopkeeper receive for a dozen chickens sold in portions rather than sold whole?

1. The weight of an unladen lorry is 2·274 tonnes. When loaded with coal the weight is 6·153 tonnes. What is the weight of the coal on the lorry?

2. While on holiday Barry weighed himself. His weight was 36·5 kg. He remembered that last year his weight was 28·75 kg. What was the increase in weight during the year?

3. Father said that he had increased by $5\frac{1}{2}$ kg in the year from 83·75 kg. What is Father's weight now?

4. A shop assistant was weighing sugar into 500 gramme packets. How many should there be from a 50 kilogramme sack?

5. How many 250 gramme packets of currants can be made up from a box containing 25 kilogrammes?

6. A kilogramme of pepper is to be made up into 50 gramme packets. How many should there be?

7. The weight of the contents of a box is marked as 0·35 kg. How many grammes is that?

8. On a shelf are nine packets of flour, each weighing 3·5 kg. There are also twelve more, each containing 0·5 kg of flour. What is the total weight of all the packets?

9. A coal merchant has to deliver 2 tonnes of coal in fifty kilo bags. How many bags must he load on to his lorry?

10. At a flour mill four lorries are loaded ready for delivering 75 sacks each the next morning. If each sack contains 50 kilogrammes of flour, what is the total weight on the lorries?

11. If during the winter a boiler uses four 50 kg sacks of coke per week, how long will $3\frac{1}{2}$ tonnes last?

12. A farmer has $22\frac{1}{2}$ tonnes of wheat to be delivered to a mill. It is decided that a lorry should make five journeys to collect the wheat. How much should there be on each load?

13. What is one-fifth of thirteen point five kilogrammes?

14. There are nine packets of wool. If each weighs 3·75 kg., what is the total weight of the packets?

These clocks show the time at which a train should leave Old-town in the morning and the time it should arrive at Newtown.

1. State how long the journey should take.

2. The train is twelve minutes late in leaving Oldtown. Give the time of its departure in figures.

3. The train is eight minutes late in arriving at Newtown. Give the time of the arrival in figures.

4. Your stay in Newtown is for exactly three hours. At what time will you leave if you arrived on this train?

Here is part of a Class Time Table.

5. How much time is allowed daily for Registration and Assembly?

6. If that amount is the same for each day of the week, what is the weekly total?

7. Which is a twenty-minute lesson?

8. How much time is allowed for Mathematics?

Class M	
a.m.	
8.55	Registration and Assembly.
9.10	Music and Movement.
9.30	Mathematics.
10.15	Reading.
10.40	Milk and Recreation.
11.00	English.

Here are some details from a poster advertising a Schoolboys' Exhibition.

9. For how many hours is the exhibition open each day?

10. State in figures the date of the opening day.

11. Remembering that 26th Dec. is a Sunday, for how many weekdays is the Exhibition open?

SCHOOLBOYS' EXHIBITION

28th Dec.1991–11th Jan. 1992
9.30 a.m.–7 p.m. Daily
Closed on Sundays

1. Andrew's pocket money was three pounds fifty each week. He decided to save a half of it. How much did he spend each week?

2. What length is equal to one-third of 96 centimetres?

3. What part of 4 cakes are two cakes?

4. What part of 8 cakes are two cakes?

5. What part of 8 cakes are six cakes?

6. What part of 12 cakes are four cakes?

7. What part of four cakes is half a cake?

8. What part of a week is one day?

9. What part of $\frac{1}{2}$ kg are 250 grammes?

10. Mother needed $1\frac{1}{2}$ metres of material to re-cover each of two chairs. What was the total length she ordered?

11. A farmer decided to reduce his herd of pigs by one-fifth. If he had 140 pigs, how many was he going to sell?

12. The farmer decided to increase his flock of sheep by $\frac{1}{3}$. If he had 135 sheep, how many was he going to buy?

13. Altogether Mother bought $\frac{1}{2}$ kilogramme of sweets. She gave a quarter of them each to Ron and Rita. How much had she left for herself and Father?

14. How much of a brass rod, 5 metres long, would be left after $3\frac{1}{5}$ m had been cut from it?

15. Tom travelled $3\frac{1}{2}$ kilometres from school by 'bus and then walked $\frac{3}{4}$ km from the 'bus stop to home. How far from school did Tom live?

16. A man looking for a house is told that he should not pay in rent more than $\frac{1}{4}$ of his wage. If his wage is £125·40 per week, what is the most he should pay in rent?

17. If each of five girls agrees to share the cost of a present, what part of the price does each girl pay?

18. What part of a load is left after $\frac{5}{8}$ of it have been unloaded?

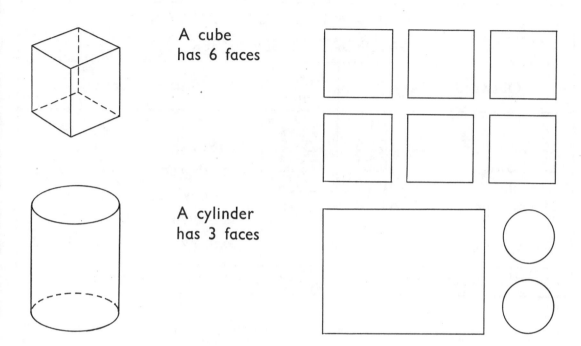

A cube
has 6 faces

A cylinder
has 3 faces

Draw the correct number of faces for each of these solids. Make your shapes approximate to the sizes shown.

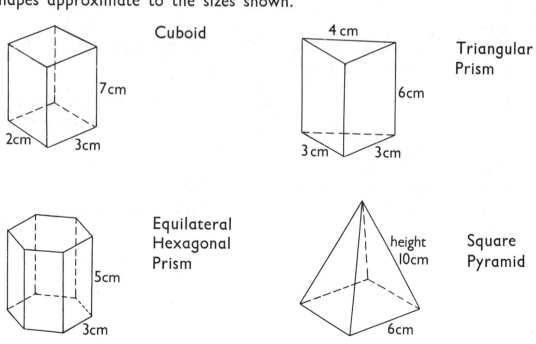

Cuboid

7 cm

2 cm   3 cm

4 cm

Triangular
Prism

6 cm

3 cm   3 cm

Equilateral
Hexagonal
Prism

5 cm

3 cm

height
10 cm

6 cm

Square
Pyramid

COALTOWN to SEATOWN SATURDAY 7th SEPTEMBER			
Outward Journey		Return fares	Return Journey	

		a.m.				p.m.
Coaltown	dep.	10 25	£2·58	Seatown	dep.	7 45
Leadtown	,,	10 31	£2·58	Mowthorpe	arr.	9 48
Thornby	,,	10 38	£2·56	Thornby	,,	10 15
Mowthorpe	,,	11 00	£2·48	Leadtown	,,	10 22
		p.m.		Coaltown	,,	10 30
Seatown	arr.	1 12				

Children under 3 yr., free; 3 yr. to under 14 yr., half-fare.

1. How long is there between the train leaving Coaltown and its leaving Leadtown?
2. Name the last stopping place before reaching Seatown.
3. How long does the train take to travel from Mowthorpe to Seatown?
4. How long does the train take to travel from Seatown to Coaltown on the return journey?
5. Which is the faster journey—outward or return?
6. If you allow 25 minutes for the journey from home, to buy your ticket and to catch the train from Coaltown, at what time should you leave home?
7. If it takes 20 minutes to travel home and the train returns on time, at what time should you reach home?
8. What should the fare be for three adults boarding the train at Coaltown?
9. State the total fares for a family from Thornby consisting of Mother and Father, Jane age 7, Mary 2, John 14 and Tom 4.
10. Using the same time intervals as on this time-table make out one for a journey from Coaltown to Seatown, leaving Coaltown at 10.55 a.m.

1. If eggs are 12p each, what should 5 eggs cost?

2. If eggs are labelled at 12p each or 4 for 45p, what is saved by buying 8 at one time instead of 8 at 12p each?

3. What should I pay for 6 boxes of matches if they are sold at 65p per dozen?

4. What would you expect to pay for one box of matches if they are sold at 65p per dozen?

5. If biscuits are priced at 92p per kilo, what would you expect to pay for a quarter kilo of them?

6. What is saved by buying a kilogramme jar at 95p instead of two half kilogramme jars at 53p each?

7. What should you pay for $3\frac{1}{2}$ kilos of sugar if a one kilogramme packet costs 65p and a half kilogramme 33p

8. Mother gave the shopkeeper a five pound note to pay for £2·75 worth of goods. What change should she receive?

9. A quarter-kilogramme packet of tea is marked at 99p, a half-kilo packet is marked at £1·95p. What would you expect to pay for $1\frac{1}{4}$ kilos of tea?

10. A shopkeeper was handed three coins for the payment of a bill for 65p. What were the values of the coins?

11. What should 200 g of sweets cost at £1·20 per half kilo?

12. Potatoes are priced at 3 kilos for 77p. What do you think the charge would be for one kilo?   for two kilos?

13. If potatoes are priced at 3 kilos for 77p, how many kilogrammes should you receive for 39p?

14. Cooked tongue is priced at £1·65 per $\frac{1}{4}$ kilo. What should be the charge for 500 g of cooked tongue?

15. Mother's groceries totalled to £2·60. What did Mother hand to the shopkeeper so that her exact change was a fifty pence coin?

Most, but not all, numbers belong to shapes.

One ● is alone.　　Two ●● is just a straight line.

Three ●●● is more than a straight line.　It can form triangles.

To make the next larger triangle we must add at least one counter to each row and, of course, put one at the top.

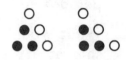

1. What is the triangle number next after 3?

2. Build up the next triangle number after 6. What is it?

3. Find out the other triangle numbers up to 30.

Square Numbers

When we come to four ●●●● we cannot arrange it into a triangle but we can use another shape, the square.

4. What is the next square number after four? Add one to each row as in the building up of triangle numbers, but this time instead of adding a single counter at the top, put a complete row.
Look carefully at the rows of counters: we have three rows of three whichever way you look at it. Think of your tables.

We say (a) that when a number is multiplied by itself it is
squared ($2 \times 2 = 4$, $3 \times 3 = 9$),

(b) that 4 and 9 are **square** numbers,

(c) that since 2 multiplied by itself gives 4,
then 2 is the **square root** of 4,
just as 3 is the **square root** of 9 ($3 \times 3 = 9$).

5. Find any other square numbers up to 30.

6. What is the square root of 36?　　of 64?

We have found that 2 counters can only make a straight line
that 3 counters can make a triangle
that 4 counters can make a square
and we know that 5 counters do not make a special shape
and that 6 counters make another triangle.

Now arrange 6 counters into a special shape, an **oblong**. There are different ways of looking at this rectangle. You may see it as 3 rows of 2 or as 2 rows of 3. $(3 \times 2 = 6$ and $2 \times 3 = 6)$

This helps you with your tables, for it proves that by learning one group you have the answer to the opposite group.

1. Which is the next rectangle number after 6?

2. Which is the next rectangle number after the square number 9?

You will find that 12 is a number which can be arranged into more than two rectangles. Many numbers are like that.

3. Copy these headings into your book and write the numbers from 1 to 30. Then put a tick against a number which can form a triangle or square or oblong.

Number	Triangle	Square	Oblong
1			
2			
3	✓		
4		✓	
5			

Some numbers cannot be formed into a rectangle, such as 1, 2, 3, 5 and several others. We call these non-rectangle numbers by a special name: **prime numbers**. A Prime Number is one that cannot be made up by multiplying two smaller numbers.

4. List the Prime Numbers from 1 to 30.

You have now met Odd Numbers, Even Numbers, Triangle Numbers, Square Numbers, Rectangle Numbers and Prime Numbers.

1. An outing has been arranged for 186 old people. If the 'buses ordered can take 204 people, how many friends or relatives can join the party?

2. What was the tax on a motor car priced at £5578 if the tax was equal to one-fifth of the selling price?

3. What will be the total distance around a triangle which has all its sides of equal length, 1·58 m?

4. What is the least length and breadth the inside of a box can be, to hold two balls side by side, each ball having a diameter of 17 cm 8 mm?

5. How many pencils are there in seven boxes if each box contains one gross?

6. If Mother allows 200 grammes of meat for each one in her family of 7 persons, what weight should she buy, $1\frac{1}{4}$ kg, $1\frac{1}{2}$ kg or $1\frac{3}{4}$ kg?

7. What is the bill for a daily paper costing 28p each weekday after being delivered for five weeks?

8. How many quarter litres equal two and a half litres?

9. When is Lucy's birthday if it is 10 days after that of Harold, which is on 26th July?

10. At what time would a forty-minute lesson begin if it was due to end at 11.15 a.m.?

11. What is the difference between the square of five and the square of six?

12. What is the answer when you take the smallest three-figure number you can make from the largest three-figure number you can make, using the figures 0, 3 and 6?

13. What must be added to one litre of milk to fill two 600 ml bottles?

14. What length of wood will be needed to make a square picture frame having each side 85 cm long?

15. How many 25 kilogramme sacks of coal equal one tonne?

16. The total cost of rail fares for 8 boys was £7·60. What was the fare for one of the boys?